the women's prize for fiction journal

this journal
belongs to:

....

the women's prize for fiction journal

celebrating 25 years

Women's
Prize for
Fiction

With special thanks to Deborah Siddoway

First published in 2021

Unbound
Level 1, Devonshire House, One Mayfair Place, London W1J 8AJ
www.unbound.com

www.womensprizeforfiction.co.uk
@WomensPrize

Illustrations and text design by Victoria Sawdon & Paul Sparrow

A CIP record for this book is available from the British Library

ISBN 978-1-80018-055-0 (hardback)

Printed in Slovenia by DZS

9 8 7 6 5 4 3 2 1

'If there's a book that you want to read, but it hasn't been written yet, then you must write it.'

—

Toni Morrison (1931–2019)

Introduction by the Women's Prize for Fiction
Founder Director, *Kate Mosse* *xii*

The 'Bessie' *xviii*

....

The Women's Prize for Fiction Winning Novels
1996–2020, with space for your own notes

contents

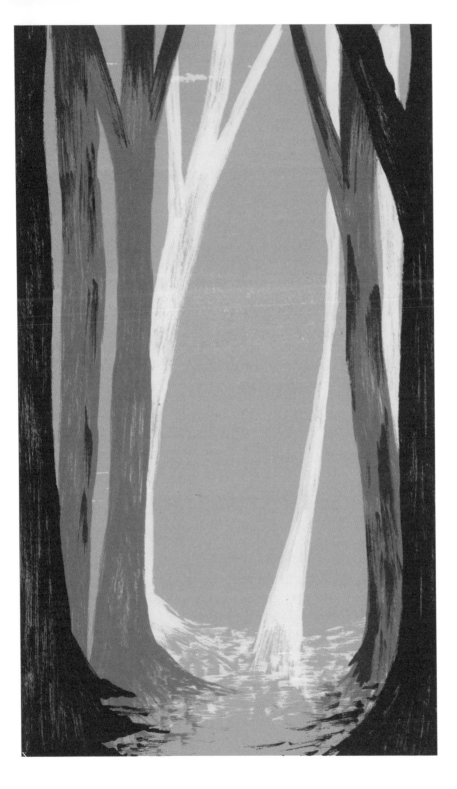

'The very reason I write is so that I might not sleepwalk through my entire life.'

—

Zadie Smith, 2006 winner

introduction

Beautiful, exquisite, brilliant, dazzling, heart-stopping,
exhilarating, life-changing, complex, challenging,
entertaining novels transform our lives. Great writing
– of imagination and ambition – inspires us, extends
our horizons. Fiction can – does – make a difference
to how we think, how we feel. To what we understand.
Novels bridge the gap between our own lives and those
of others past and present, those with different lived
experiences from our own. In the pages of a book, we
can travel anywhere in the world, stand in one another's
shoes, engage with myriad other realities and times.
Novels slip between the gaps of what can and what
cannot be said; they help us to think, to listen.

To put women's voices centre stage was just one of many
reasons we set up the Women's Prize for Fiction twenty-
five years ago. Our aims then, as now, were simple: first,
to honour, amplify and celebrate exceptional, original
and beautiful fiction written by women in English from
all over the world – genre no object, age no object,

ethnicity no object, country of birth or residence no object, background no object, subject matter no object; second, to ensure that women's creative endeavours were visible and properly acknowledged, that women's work took up space on the bookshelves; third, to use the razzamatazz (and, yes, sometimes the controversy of a Prize set up by women to celebrate women) to fund and promote a range of charitable, educational and major research projects focusing on reading, diversifying and extending writing and engagement opportunities for women and girls. Finally, to put the classics of tomorrow in the hands of the readers of today.

In this quarter of a century, we've gone from being the new kid on the literary block to the largest (and one of the most joyous!) annual celebrations of women's literary creativity anywhere in the world. We've worked with amazing sponsors and partners to promote a programme of charitable and ambitiously innovative projects from community and workplace reading groups to writing and mentoring initiatives. We've invested in new platforms to break down barriers, to increase access, to create a digital hub of readers and writers, to ensure that as wide and diverse an audience as possible can engage with the Prize and feel it belongs to them. We've listened and learned, expanded and adapted, to build a year-round creative community celebrating women's voices. Details of our programme of events are on our website, www.womensprizeforfiction.co.uk, together with reading tips, interviews with a wide range of inspirational women; plenty of advice on writing and publishing, as well as information about ways in which women can get involved and support the Prize for the future.

So, this journal is a celebration. Of the twenty-five exceptional novels that have, so far, won the Women's Prize for Fiction as well as a salute to all those yet to come. It's a celebration of the thousands of women who've made the Prize what it is, working behind the scenes or out front, giving their time as judges or taking part in events; booksellers and librarians, publishers and journalists, campaigners and activists. It's a celebration of women standing shoulder to shoulder with other women, reminding us that women's unheard stories matter, that women's underheard voices matter even more. It's a celebration of the millions of readers who have bought, borrowed or shared a WPFF-longlisted, shortlisted or winning novel and found their hearts moved, their minds inspired, their perspectives altered.

But, most of all, this journal is about you. As well as words from writers of the past and present, writing tips and advice, there are beautiful blank pages waiting for your thoughts, your sketched ideas, the earliest glimmerings of your first short story or memoir. Perhaps this is where your own first novel will take flight.

Times have changed since we began our mission. The challenges and priorities when we set up the Prize are not the same now. But the need – as women – to support other women for the benefit of all, to ensure women's voices of excellence and brilliance continue to be heard, that women's creative endeavour is rewarded and acknowledged, this has not changed. If anything, it matters more now than ever.

The Women's Prize helps ensure that all women's voices are heard, honoured and celebrated. So fill this journal with your own words. Write what you imagine, what you feel, what you fear, what you dream, and don't hold back.

Be ambitious, be bold, be yourself.

Kate Mosse, Novelist and Playwright,
Founder Director of the Women's Prize for Fiction

Join the conversation at www.womensprizeforfiction.co.uk or @WomensPrize

The Prize was known as the Orange Prize for Fiction between 1996 and 2012, the Women's Prize for Fiction in 2013, the Baileys Women's Prize for Fiction from 2014 to 2017 and, since 2018, has reverted to the Women's Prize for Fiction. For clarity, we have used Women's Prize throughout.

'Reading is the key that opens doors to many good things in life. Reading shaped my dreams, and more reading helped me make my dreams come true.'

—

Ruth Bader Ginsberg (1933–2020)

the
'bessie'

Each winner of the Women's Prize for Fiction receives a cheque for £30,000 and a 'Bessie'. Each is unique, cast in a slightly different coloured bronze each year, and is taken from a cast donated by the late Grizel Niven (1906–2007), a sculptor and artist who studied at the Slade School in the 1920s. There are also three silver Bessies, cast by Jaspar Lyon. The first was awarded to Andrea Levy's *Small Island* as the 'best of the best' of our first decade; the second was presented to Chimamanda Ngozi Adichie's *Half of a Yellow Sun* for the second decade. *Half of a Yellow Sun* also won the third silver Bessie on the occasion of our twenty-fifth anniversary in 2020.

The 'Bessie' (named by the anonymous donor who, in the mid-1990s, established the Trust fund to provide the prize money in perpetuity), is about 19cm tall. The original sculpture is nearly a metre high and stood in Niven's garden in Chelsea, London. Niven died at the age of 100 and the anonymous donor – for whom the Bessie is named – passed away a few years after the Prize was launched. We are very grateful to them for their generosity and support. It is in the spirit of the Women's Prize for Fiction that it was two women, of a much older generation, who helped support a group of young women to get the prize started.

'I have always been one hundred per cent behind the Prize ever since its inception. Of all the book prizes, there is a real feeling of mutual support. It's a showcase and it's a celebration; it's more than just a competition.'

—

Hilary Mantel, Shortlisted 2006, 2010, 2013, 2020

a spell
of winter
helen
dunmore

1996

Catherine and her brother Rob don't know
why they have been abandoned by their parents.
Alone in their grandfather's decaying country house,
they roam the wild grounds freely, with minds attuned
to the rural wilderness. Lost in their own private world,
they seek and find new lines to cross.

But as the First World War draws closer, crimes both
big and small threaten the delicate refuge they have
built. Cathy will do anything to protect their dark Eden
from anyone, or anything, that threatens to destroy it.

*Helen Dunmore (1952–2017) was an award-winning novelist,
children's author, short story writer and poet; and Fellow of the
Royal Society of Literature. She published twelve novels, including*
Zennor in Darkness, *which won the McKitterick Prize;*
Burning Bright; A Spell of Winter, *which won the inaugural
Women's Prize in 1996;* Talking to the Dead; Your Blue-
Eyed Boy; With Your Crooked Heart; The Siege, *which
was shortlisted for the 2001 Whitbread Novel of the Year Award
and the Women's Prize 2002;* Mourning Ruby; *and* House
of Orphans. *She was posthumously awarded the Costa 2017
prize for her poetry collection* Inside the Wave. *Dunmore was a
judge for the Women's Prize in 2015.*

'Were she alive now, Helen would no doubt be celebrating the 25th anniversary of the Women's Prize and the women whose writing has been recognised by it, and would still feel gratitude for the encouragement and inspiration that the prize gave her.'

Patrick Dunmore, Helen Dunmore's son

'Helen Dunmore was our very first winner for a beautiful novel. It's one of those lyrical, haunting novels that stay with you long after you have finished it.'

Kate Mosse, Chair of Judges 1996
and Founder Director of the Women's Prize for Fiction

fugitive
pieces
anne
michaels

1997

Jakob Beer is seven years old when he is rescued from the muddy ruins of a buried village in Nazi-occupied Poland.

Of his family, he is the only one who has survived. Under the guidance of the Greek geologist Athos, Jakob must steel himself to excavate the horrors of his own history.

A novel of astounding beauty and wisdom, *Fugitive Pieces* is a profound meditation on the resilience of the human spirit and love's ability to resurrect even the most damaged of hearts.

Anne Michaels is an award-winning novelist and poet. She was born in Toronto in 1958 and educated at Toronto University where she continues to teach as an adjunct professor of creative writing. Her first volume of poems, The Weight of Oranges, *was published to great acclaim in 1986 when it won the Commonwealth Poetry Prize for the Americas. She has published several other books of poetry, including the award-winning* Miner's Pond *and* Skin Divers. Fugitive Pieces, *her first novel, has been published in over thirty countries and, as well as the Women's Prize, has won many international awards, including both the Guardian Fiction Award and the Lannan Literary Award.*

'I was astonished to be shortlisted
and felt complete shock at winning.
After the ceremony, I was overwhelmed
by the sudden realisation that this book,
which had taken everything, might
now find a readership. I cannot express
the gratitude I felt at this, and the hope
it contained. The encouragement of
the prize to this day moves me more
than I can say.'

Anne Michaels

'*Fugitive Pieces* is a most extraordinary
novel because it goes viscerally to the
heart of the survivors of any disaster…
The poet in Anne Michaels turns
suffering into celebration.'

Lisa Jardine, Chair of Judges 1997

'There is no greater agony than bearing an untold story inside you.'

—

Maya Angelou (1928–2014)

larry's
party
carol
shields

1998

Larry, and his naïve young wife Dorrie, spend their
honeymoon in England. In the ordered riotousness
of Hampton Court's maze, Larry Weller discovers
the passion of his life.

Perhaps his ever-growing obsession with mazes
may help him find a way through the bewilderment
deepening about him as – through twenty years
and two failed marriages – he endeavours to
understand his own needs, and those of friends,
parents, lovers and a growing son.

*Carol Shields (1935–2003) was a multi-award-winning
American-born Canadian novelist and short story writer. As well
as* Larry's Party, *her novels include* Unless, *shortlisted for the
2003 Women's Prize;* The Stone Diaries, *winner of the
Pulitzer Prize for Fiction and shortlisted for the Booker Prize;*
The Republic of Love; Happenstance; *and* Mary Swann.
Her short story collections Dressing Up for the Carnival
and Various Miracles *were republished alongside previously
unpublished works in one volume,* The Collected Stories,
*in 2004. Born in Illinois and brought up in Chicago,
Carol Shields lived in Canada from 1957 until her death.*

'Carol had been on prize long-
and shortlists before the winner
of the prize was announced in 1998.
Larry's Party had been shortlisted for
Canada's prestigious Giller Prize
and nominated for the Guardian
Fiction Prize. But Carol viewed
winning this prize for *Larry's Party*
as a crucial milestone in her career,
and a considerable factor in expanding
interest in her work and in the ideas
that were important to her.'

The Shields Family

'What she does is explore the
infinite complexity of those
aspects of ordinary life…'

Sheena Macdonald, Chair of Judges 1998

a crime
in the
neighborhood
suzanne
berne

1999

In the long hot summer of 1972, three events shattered the serenity of ten-year-old Marsha's life: her father ran away with her mother's sister Ada; Boyd Ellison, a young boy, was molested and murdered; and Watergate made the headlines.

Living in a world no longer safe or familiar, Marsha turns increasingly to 'the book of evidence' in which she records the doings of the neighbours, especially of shy Mr Green next door. But as Marsha's confusion and her murder hunt accelerate, her 'facts' spread the damage cruelly and catastrophically throughout the neighbourhood.

Born in Virginia in 1961 and then moving to Washington, DC, when she was ten, Suzanne Berne worked as a journalist before completing an MFA in creative writing at University of Iowa Writers' Workshop. A series of short-lived jobs in California followed, ranging from hostess at a San Francisco restaurant to proof-reader for the Hollywood Reporter, *before returning to the East Coast to teach at Harvard University. As well as* A Crime in the Neighborhood, *her books include* Ghost at the Table, A Perfect Arrangement, Missing Lucile: Memories of the Grandmother I Never Knew *and* Dogs of Littlefield. *Her short fiction and essays have appeared in a number of magazines. She currently teaches creative writing at Boston College.*

'Everyone should get one truly thrilling experience in life, and the few days I spent in Britain before the prize was awarded were mine. It was fun and exciting, very much a "once in a lifetime" moment. I think it was the first time I really saw myself as a novelist. Not as a student or teacher or mother or an "aspiring" anything, but as a novelist.'

Suzanne Berne

'It's a real achievement to have [a murder] at the centre of the text without it dominating everything in an unsubtle way.'

Lola Young, Chair of Judges 1999

'There are two different ways
to approach writing. The first
is engineered. This approach is
more mathematical and focuses
on structure. These writers like
to know everything that is going
to happen before they start
writing. The second way is
to follow your instincts.
I have always felt closer
to the second path.'

—

Elif Shafak

when i
lived in
modern
times
linda
grant

2000

It is April 1946. Evelyn Sert, twenty years old,
a hairdresser from Soho, sails for Palestine,
where Jewish refugees and idealists are gathering
from across Europe to start a new life in a brand
new country.

In the glittering, cosmopolitan, Bauhaus city
of Tel Aviv, anything seems possible – a new self,
new Jew, new woman are all feasible. Evelyn, adept
at disguises, reinvents herself as the bleached-blonde
Priscilla Jones. Immersed in a world of passionate
idealism, she discovers love, and with Johnny,
her lover, finds herself at the heart of a very
dangerous game.

Linda Grant was born in Liverpool in 1951. As well as
When I Lived in Modern Times, *which was also
shortlisted for the Jewish Quarterly Wingate Literary
Prize, her novels include* The Clothes on Their Backs,
*shortlisted for the Man Booker Prize in 2008 and winner of
the South Bank Show Literature Award;* The Dark Circle,
shortlisted for the Women's Prize for Fiction in 2017; and
A Stranger City *(2019). Her non-fiction books include
her memoir* Remind Me Who I Am Again, *winner of
both the Mind and Age Concern Book of the Year awards;*
Sexting the Millennium; The People on the Street:
A Writer's View of Israel, *which won the Lettre Ulysses
Prize for the Art of Reportage; and* The Thoughtful
Dresser. *She is a Fellow of the Royal Society of Literature
and lives in London.*

'I'd been at the very first Orange Prize,
when Helen Dunmore won. Even then,
I thought: "Yeah, I want this." *When I Lived
in Modern Times* had only been out a couple
of months when the surprise of the longlist
arrived. The night of the party was spectacular.
I vaguely remember that there were acrobats.
When my name was announced I remember
walking into a blaze of flashlights, and the roar
of the photographers calling my name. I hadn't
prepared a speech. I said something about how
what writing is really about is getting up on
a cold morning and putting on your leggings
and sweater and staring at a blank screen.
The moment of winning a prize might
be a culmination of that, but the gulf
between the two states is vast.'

Linda Grant

'The idea of a whole new start, and a whole new
world, is a tremendously optimistic and puzzling
beginning, but then reality impinges. It takes us
into this whole world of the foundation of Israel…
it's tremendously convincing.'

Polly Toynbee, Chair of Judges 2000

'You do not have to write every day! The age-old advice that a writer must write daily is very discouraging to people who work for a living, care for others or do any sort of labour that does not afford them long stretches of unmolested time. In my opinion, the very activities and interests that keep a writer from her desk are the things that will enrich her writing when she does sit down to create. So my advice is to write frequently.'

—

Tayari Jones, 2019 Winner

'Ask yourself what risk you are not taking – and then take that risk. Push yourself to find what is true for your characters, what is left unsaid at the heart of the story you are wanting to tell. Experiment. Play. Make us laugh, and then make us cry.'

—

A.M. Homes, 2013 Winner

' Terrify yourself
at least a little with
every new project.'

Kamila Shamsie, 2018 Winner

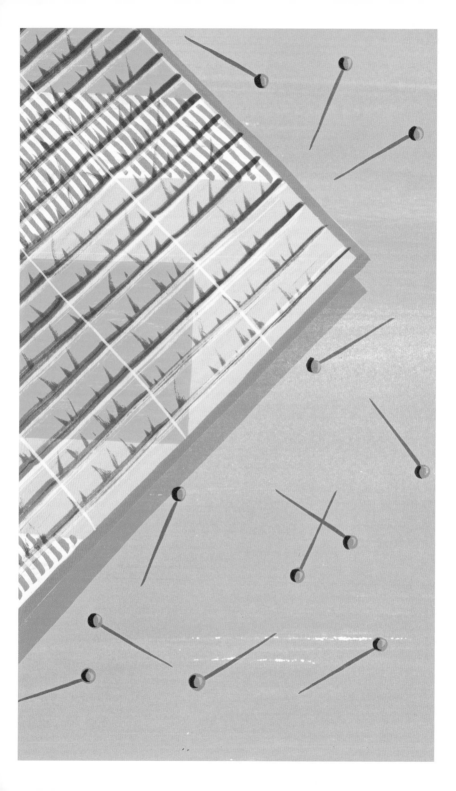

the
idea
of
perfection

kate
grenville

2001

The Idea of Perfection is a funny and touching romance between two people who've given up on love. Set in the eccentric little backwater of Karakarook, New South Wales, pop. 1,374, it tells the story of Douglas Cheeseman, a gawky engineer with jug-handle ears, and Harley Savage, a woman altogether too big and too abrupt for comfort.

Harley has come to Karakarook to help establish a heritage museum. Douglas is there to pull down the quaint old Bent Bridge. From day one, they're on a collision course. But out of this unpromising conjunction of opposites, something unexpected happens, which is sometimes even better than perfection. It's a novel about the human impulse to conceal our weaknesses from ourselves as well as each other, and the fact that life really starts when we stop trying to be perfect.

Kate Grenville is an Australian author of nine novels and six non-fiction books, including her novel A Room Made of Leaves, *which gives a voice to one of the many silenced women of history. She has an international readership, and is the winner of many prizes.* The Secret River, *which sparked controversy in her home country, and became a bestseller, also won the Commonwealth Writers' Prize and was shortlisted for the Man Booker Prize. Her three books about the craft of writing have become classics for Creative Writing courses.*

'I'd published five novels to critical acclaim, but modest sales. I was facing the fact that for financial reasons I'd have to give up writing and become a full-time teacher of creative writing. The other shortlisted books that year were by supremely good writers (including Ali Smith and Margaret Atwood) and it never crossed my mind that I might win. That meant I could relax and enjoy the fact that the humour of the book obviously spoke to British audiences as well as Australian ones. The prize gave me a breathing-space. In quite a direct way, it enabled me to go on writing, when without it I would have had to stop.'

Kate Grenville

'An exquisite, minutely observed study of two people meeting in their middle years... A truly amazing writer.'

Rosie Boycott, Chair of Judges 2001

'Perhaps it is just as well to be rash and foolish for a while. If writers were too wise, perhaps no books would get written at all.'

—

Zora Neale Hurston (1891–1960)

bel
canto
ann
patchett

2002

Latin American terrorists storm an international gathering hosted by an underprivileged country to promote foreign interest and trade, only to find that their intended target, the President, has stayed home to watch his favourite soap opera on TV. Among the hostages are a world-class opera singer and her biggest fan, a Japanese tycoon who has been persuaded to attend the party on the understanding that she will perform half a dozen arias after dinner. The tycoon's engaging and sympathetic translator plays a vital role in the subsequent relationships between so many different nationalities closeted together, interpreting not only the terrorists' negotiations but also the language of love between lovers who cannot understand what the other is saying. Ultimately, it is the terrorist strike that does more to promote foreign relations than anyone could have hoped to achieve with the party.

Award-winning novelist and non-fiction author Ann Patchett is the author of eight novels: Bel Canto, The Patron Saint of Liars, Taft, Run, The Magician's Assistant *and* State of Wonder *(both shortlisted for the Women's Prize),* Commonwealth *and* The Dutch House. *She was the editor of* Best American Short Stories of 2006, *and has written three books of non-fiction:* Truth and Beauty, *about her friendship with the writer Lucy Grealy;* What Now?; *and* This is the Story of a Happy Marriage, *a collection of essays examining the theme of commitment. In 2019, she published her first children's book,* Lambslide, *illustrated by Robin Preiss Glasser. In November 2011, she opened Parnassus Books in Nashville, Tennessee, where she lives with her husband Karl Van Devender and their dog Sparky.*

'I was on the long- and shortlist three times and fully expected to lose again. My husband and father and stepmother were with me, and my two elderly English cousins came from Yorkshire for the award ceremony. One cousin was a Catholic priest, Father Bernard, and he and his sister Marie were staying in a convent in London. He told me just before the ceremony that he had asked all the nuns to pray for me to win. I felt I'd cheated because I had a whole flock of praying nuns and the other finalists didn't. At least not that I knew of.

'Even now, I'll be dusting in the living room and I'll pick up that little statue [the Bessie] and think about what a happy moment that was. My father is dead now, as are the elderly English cousins. I think about how happy they were that night. I had begged them not to come because I thought they'd be sad when I lost, but then I won and they were there. It was beautiful.'

Ann Patchett

'This is a fine piece of writing, mixing tenderness and danger to an impressive degree.'

Sue MacGregor, Chair of Judges 2002

property

valerie

martin

2003

Manon Gaudet is unhappily married to the owner of a Louisiana sugar plantation. She misses her family and longs for the vibrant lifestyle of her native New Orleans, but most of all, she longs to be free of the suffocating domestic situation. The tension revolves around Sarah, an enslaved girl who may have been 'given' to Manon as a wedding present from her aunt, and whose young son Walter is living proof of where Manon's husband's inclinations lie.

This private drama is being played out against a brooding atmosphere of unrest and bloody uprisings. And if the attacks reach Manon's house, no one can be sure which way Sarah will turn.

Beautifully written, *Property* is an intricately told tale of both individual stories and a country in a time of change, where ownership is at once everything and nothing, and where belonging, by contrast, is all.

Valerie Martin was born in Missouri and raised in New Orleans. She is the author of eleven novels, including The Ghost of the Mary Celeste, The Confessions of Edward Day, Trespass, Mary Reilly, Italian Fever *and* Property*; four collections of short fiction; and a biography of Saint Francis of Assisi, as well as children's books. She has taught at US universities, including the University of Alabama, the University of Massachusetts Amherst and Sarah Lawrence College. She has been awarded many literary prizes and awards, including grants from the National Endowment for the Arts and the John Simon Guggenheim Fellowship, and the Kafka Prize.*

'The week before the prize lives in my memory as a very bright and bubbly adventure. I truly didn't expect to win. The night of the award ceremony, my fellow American finalist Donna Tartt and I found ourselves standing near the stage, drinks and purses in hand. We shared our anxiety about going on the stage carrying a purse. Quickly we agreed that if she won I would take her purse and if I won she would take mine. When the winner was announced, the speaker's voice was so low I couldn't hear it. Donna said, "It's you," and reached for my purse. I was truly surprised and enormously pleased. Somewhere along the line I had made a list of names to say thank you to and tucked it into my waistband. Excellent foresight!'

Valerie Martin

'A novel which deals with a huge subject with originality… [it] performs the difficult task of depicting dramatic events with stylish restraint.'

Ahdaf Soueif, Chair of Judges 2003

'This has always been a man's world, and none of the reasons that have been offered in explanation have seemed adequate.'

—

Simone de Beauvoir (1908–1986)

small island
andrea levy

2004

It is 1948, and England is recovering from a war. But at 21 Nevern Street, London, the conflict has only just begun. Queenie Bligh's neighbours do not approve when she agrees to take in Jamaican lodgers, but Queenie doesn't know when her husband will return, or if he will come back at all. What else can she do?

Gilbert Joseph was one of the several thousand Jamaican men who joined the RAF to fight against Hitler. Returning to England as a civilian, he finds himself treated very differently. It's desperation that makes him remember a wartime friendship with Queenie and knock at her door.

Gilbert's wife Hortense, too, had longed to leave Jamaica and start a better life in England. But when she joins him she is shocked to find London shabby, decrepit, and far from the golden city of her dreams. Even Gilbert is not the man she thought he was…

Andrea Levy (1956–2019) was born in England to Jamaican parents who came to Britain in 1948. After attending writing workshops when she was in her mid-thirties, Levy began to write the novels that she, as a young woman, had always wanted to read – entertaining novels that reflected the experience of black Britons, which look at Britain and its changing population, and the intimacies that bind British history with that of the Caribbean. As well as Small Island, *which also won the Whitbread Book of the Year and the Commonwealth Writers' Prize, she was the author of six books, including* Every Light in the House Burnin', Never Far from Nowhere *(which was longlisted for the Women's Prize),* Fruit of the Lemon *and* The Long Song, *which won the Walter Scott Prize and was shortlisted for the Man Booker Prize. Her last book was* Six Stories and an Essay. Small Island *was awarded the accolade of 'Best of the Best' of the first decade of the Women's Prize, and was adapted into a television series and a stage production. Andrea Levy was a judge of the Women's Prize in 1997.*

'Sixteen years have passed since the win and Andrea is no longer here to describe it herself, but I know just what she would have said. The prize ceremony took place in a massive marquee hastily erected on a piece of open ground just across the road from the Royal Festival Hall. Many times after that night Andrea and I would pass by that spot (now a car park) and she would say to me: "This is where my life changed." The change was much more than book sales and media attention. It was a profound shift in her sense of self. Her writing had always been her way of struggling to make visible her Caribbean heritage and to challenge its marginal place in British society. Winning the prize felt like a recognition, from that very society; and that massively boosted her confidence and widened her ambition.'

Bill Mayblin, Andrea Levy's husband

'An astonishing tour de force... Juggling four voices, she illuminates a little-known aspect of recent British history with wit and wisdom.'

Sandi Toksvig, Chair of Judges 2004

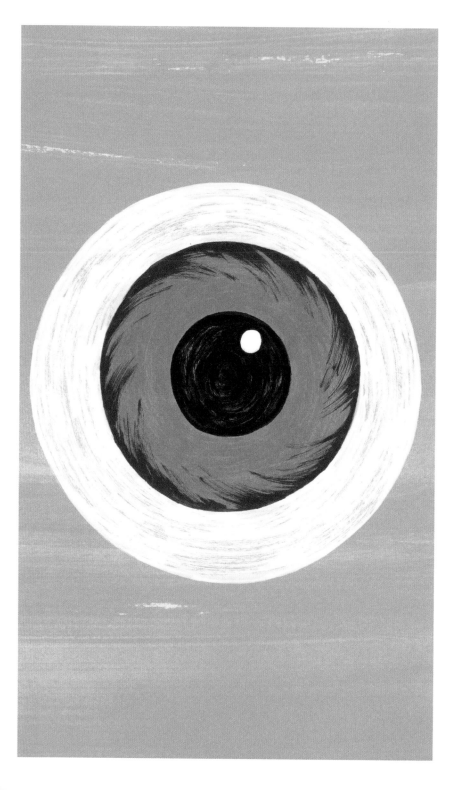

we need
to talk
about
kevin

lionel
shriver

2005

Eva never really wanted to be a mother; certainly not the mother of the unlovable boy who murdered seven of his fellow high-school students, a cafeteria worker and a teacher who tried to befriend him.

Now, two years later, it is time for her to come to terms with marriage, career, family, parenthood and Kevin's horrific rampage in a series of startlingly direct correspondences with her absent husband, Franklyn. Uneasy with the sacrifices and social demotion of motherhood from the start, Eva fears that her alarming dislike for her own son may have been responsible for driving him so nihilistically off the rails.

Lionel Shriver was born in North Carolina and now lives in London and Brooklyn, NY. As well as We Need to Talk About Kevin, *she is the author of sixteen novels including* The Post-Birthday World, Big Brother, Ordinary Decent Criminals *and* The Motion of the Body Through Space. *She is widely published as a journalist, writing features, columns, op-eds and book reviews for many publications.*

'I'd never been shortlisted for a prize in my life. After now having been shortlisted for more than one major literary prize, I can testify to the obvious in hindsight: winning is better than losing. The instant someone else's name is announced, it's suddenly an ordinary Wednesday evening (and you want to go home). Instead, 2005 was exhilarating. My husband and I stayed up until 6 a.m.'

Lionel Shriver

'No other writer has [Shriver's] acerbic turn of phrase, nor the courage to examine so forensically the ambivalence felt by so many mothers.'

Jenni Murray, Chair of Judges 2005

'I have chosen to no longer be apologetic for my femaleness and my femininity.
And I want to be respected in all of my femaleness because I deserve to be.'
—

Chimamanda Ngozi Adichie, 2007 Winner

' My very favourite tip comes from my friend Elizabeth Gilbert in her book *Big Magic*. She says everyone says they want to write but they don't have the time. Liz says you'd find the time if you were having an affair, even if it was just to grab fifteen minutes in a dark hallway. I love that. Let writing be at least as important as an affair. Find the time.'

Ann Patchett, 2002 Winner

' Understand why you are writing,
write towards that aim.'

Anne Michaels, 1997 Winner

on
beauty
zadie
smith

2006

Set between New England and London, *On Beauty* is a brilliantly funny and deeply moving story about love and family that concerns a pair of feuding families – the Belseys and the Kipps – and a clutch of doomed affairs. It puts low morals among high ideals and asks some searching questions about what life does to love. For the Belseys and the Kipps, the confusions – both personal and political – of their uncertain age are about to be brought close to home: right to the heart of family.

Zadie Smith was born in north-west London in 1975. As well as winning for On Beauty, *her novels* White Teeth *and* The Autograph Man *were shortlisted for the Women's Prize in 2000 and 2003 respectively. Her other novels include* NW, Swing Time *and* The Embassy of Cambodia, *as well as essay collections* Changing My Mind *and* Intimations: Six Essays. *She is also the editor of* The Book of Other People *and a fellow of the Royal Society of Literature, and has twice been listed as one of Granta's 20 Best Young British Novelists. As well as the Women's Prize for Fiction, she has won many awards, including the Whitbread First Novel Award and the Guardian First Book Award, and has been shortlisted for the Man Booker Prize. After spending several years in New York, she now lives in London.*

'Winning gave me a sense of stability and acceptance, but also a great desire to keep moving in a different direction. I suppose public acceptance makes me feel a little nervous – and that's a good thing. Anxiety and fear fuel creativity, at least in my case. It gave me confidence to move ahead.'

Zadie Smith

'A book which combines extraordinary characterisation with skilful and seemingly effortless plotting…
It's extremely funny, in the way that it is full of gentle parody. There is more and more in it each time you read it.'

Martha Kearney, Chair of Judges 2006

half of a
yellow sun
chimamanda ngozi adichie

2007

In 1960s Nigeria, a country blighted by civil war, three lives intersect.

Ugwu, a boy from a poor village, works as a houseboy for a university professor. Olanna, a young woman, has abandoned her life of privilege in Lagos to live with her charismatic new lover, the professor. And Richard, a shy English writer, is in thrall to Olanna's enigmatic twin sister. As the horrific Biafran War engulfs them, they are thrown together and pulled apart in ways they had never imagined.

Chimamanda Ngozi Adichie's masterpiece is a novel about Africa in a wider sense: about the end of colonialism, ethnic allegiances, class and race – and about the ways in which love can complicate all of these things.

Chimamanda Ngozi Adichie is the author of award-winning and bestselling novels, including Purple Hibiscus, *which was shortlisted for the Women's Prize in 2004;* Americanah; *the short story collection* The Thing Around Your Neck; *and the essay* We Should All Be Feminists. *A recipient of a MacArthur Fellowship, she divides her time between the United States and Nigeria.* Half of a Yellow Sun *was acclaimed the 'Best of the Best' of the second decade of the Women's Prize for Fiction.*

'I remember being happy about being on the longlist. I told myself I shouldn't hope too much, so I could protect myself from disappointment. But of course, I hoped to be on the shortlist. And when I heard I was, I remember thinking: this is wonderful validation. It's enough. And in some ways it really was. Still, to hear my name announced was an utterly glorious experience. I couldn't wait to get off stage and call my father.'

Chimamanda Ngozi Adichie

'… an astonishing feat. Chimamanda's achievement makes *Half of a Yellow Sun* not just a worthy winner of this most special of prizes, but a benchmark for excellence in fiction writing.'

Muriel Gray, Chair of Judges 2007

'Books mean all possibilities. They mean moving out of yourself, losing yourself, dying of thirst and living to your full. They mean everything.'
—

Ali Smith, 2015 Winner

the road home

rose tremain

2008

Lev is on his way from Eastern Europe to Britain, seeking work. Behind him loom the figures of his dead wife, his beloved young daughter and his outrageous friend Rudi who – dreaming of the wealthy West – lives largely for his battered Chevrolet. Ahead of Lev lies the deep strangeness of the British: their hostile streets, their clannish pubs, their obsession with celebrity.

London holds out the alluring possibility of friendship, sex, money and a new career and, if Lev is lucky, a new sense of belonging…

Rose Tremain, born in London in 1943, was one of only five women writers to be included in Granta's original list of 20 Best of Young British Novelists in 1983. Her novels and short stories have been published worldwide in twenty-seven countries and, in addition to the Women's Prize, she has won many awards, including the Sunday Express Book of the Year Award (for Restoration, *also shortlisted for the Booker Prize); the James Tait Black Memorial Prize (for* Sacred Country*); and the Whitbread Novel of the Year Award (for* Music and Silence*). She was made a Dame of the British Empire in 2020 and lives in Norfolk.*

'I was shortlisted in 2004, for my novel *The Colour*. That year, the prize rightly went to the late Andrea Levy for *Small Island*. But it was good to carry the prize home in 2008. That our times have produced so many great female fiction writers doesn't mean we don't need a Women's Prize to celebrate our collective endeavours. And new young female writers are following us.'

Rose Tremain

'A powerfully imagined story and a wonderful feat of emotional empathy told with great warmth and humour... It is an incredibly important book, about one of the biggest issues facing our society today: migration... She had a lot of foresight.'

Kirsty Lang, Chair of Judges 2008

home

marilynne robinson

2009

Jack Boughton, prodigal son, has been gone twenty years. He returns home to seek refuge and to make peace with the past. A bad boy from childhood, an alcoholic who cannot hold down a job, Jack is perpetually at odds with his surroundings and with his traditionalist father, though he remains Boughton's most beloved child. His sister Glory has also returned, fleeing her own mistakes, to care for their dying father. A moving book about families, about love and death and faith, *Home* is unforgettable.

Marilynne Robinson is the award-winning author of five novels and six works of non-fiction. She is the recipient of a 2012 National Humanities Medal, and in 2013, she was awarded South Korea's Pak Kyong-ni Prize for her contribution to international literature. Her first novel, Housekeeping, *won the Hemingway Foundation/PEN Award;* Lila *won the National Book Critics Circle Award; and* Gilead *won both the 2005 Pulitzer Prize for Fiction and the National Book Critics Circle Award. Robinson's non-fiction books include* Mother Country, *which was nominated for a National Book Award, and* What Are We Doing Here? *She lives in Iowa City where she taught at the University of Iowa Writers' Workshop for twenty-five years.*

'It is a wonderful institution and it's certainly the most elegant, brilliant platform for women's literature that I can really imagine… I just write what's on my mind and I'm extremely grateful for the fact that other people seem to find it meaningful to them also; it seems almost miraculous to me.'

Marilynne Robinson

'A kind, wise, enriching novel, exquisitely crafted. We were unanimously agreed; it is a profound work of art.'

Fi Glover, Chair of Judges 2009

'There are some words that once spoken will split the world in two. There would be the life before you breathed them and then the altered life after they'd been said. They take a long time to find, words like that. They make you hesitate. Choose with care.'

—

Andrea Levy (1956–2019)

the
lacuna
barbara
kingsolver

2010

This is the heart-breaking story of a man torn between the warm heart of Mexico and the cold embrace of 1950s America in the shadow of Senator Joseph McCarthy. Born in the US and raised in Mexico, Harrison Shepherd is a liability to his social-climbing flapper mother, Salome. When he starts work in the household of Mexican artists Diego Rivera and Frida Kahlo – where the Bolshevik leader Lev Trotsky is also being harboured as a political exile – he inadvertently casts in his lot with art, communism and revolution. A compulsive diarist, he records and relates his colourful experiences of life with Rivera, Kahlo and Trotsky in the midst of the Mexican revolution. A violent upheaval sends him back to the US; but political winds continue to throw him between north and south, in a plot that turns many times on the unspeakable breach – the lacuna – between truth and public presumption.

Barbara Kingsolver's sixteen books of fiction, poetry and non-fiction include the novels The Bean Trees *and the international bestseller* The Poisonwood Bible *which, amongst other accolades, won the 2005 Penguin/Orange Reading Group Book of the Year award. Kingsolver was named one of the most important writers of the twentieth century by* Writers Digest. *In 2000, she received the National Humanities Medal, the US's highest honour for service through the arts. She grew up in Kentucky, and spent two decades in Tucson, Arizona, before moving to south-western Virginia where she currently lives.*

'I was shortlisted in 1999, for *The Poisonwood Bible*, and [was] unable to attend the ceremonies because I had a baby and overwhelming family duties at home. It felt like a bittersweet nomination for those reasons, especially for a prize meant to support female writers. But I did what we do – continued to care for my family, and to write. When *The Lacuna* was eventually shortlisted, and I was able to travel, and I won the prize, you can be sure that I felt like Cinderella at the ball.'

Barbara Kingsolver

'A book of breath-taking scale and shattering moments of poignancy.'

Daisy Goodwin, Chair of Judges 2010

' Trust your instincts. Art goes on in a part of the brain that knows what it's doing. Don't be derailed by too many creative writing course rules.'

Linda Grant, 2000 Winner

' *"I think that this task is appointed*
for you, Frodo; and that if you
do not find a way, no one will."

You have a responsibility to
the people in your head. If you
don't sit down and write their
story, no one will, and it'll stay
in your head. Bullheadedness
is what you need. Sit and write
and get it told; you can worry
about fixing it afterwards.'

—

Lisa McInerney, 2016 Winner

' Don't expect the first draft
to work, or the second, or the
tenth. Writing is a deep dive.
It's so easy to want it to be
finished, but you need to be
sure you've travelled the whole
way. Sometimes that means
throwing out material that's
perfectly well-written, except
that it's wrong for the story.'

Madeline Miller, 2012 Winner

the
tiger's
wife

téa
obreht

A tiger escapes from the local zoo, padding through the ruined streets and onwards, to a ridge above the Balkan village of Galina. His nocturnal visits hold the villagers in a terrified thrall – but for one boy, the tiger is a thing of magic.

Natalia is the granddaughter of that boy. Now a doctor, she is visiting orphanages in the war-torn Balkans when she receives word of her beloved grandfather's death, far from their home, in circumstances shrouded in mystery.

Compelled to unravel the truth, Natalia stumbles upon a clue that will lead her to a tattered copy of *The Jungle Book*, and then to the most extraordinary story her grandfather never told her – the legend of the tiger's wife.

Téa Obreht is the youngest ever winner of the Women's Prize. She was born in Belgrade, in the former Yugoslavia, in 1985 and moved to the United States at the age of twelve. She currently lives in New York City and teaches at Hunter College. Obreht was a National Book Foundation 5 Under 35 honoree and was named by The New Yorker *as one of the twenty best American fiction writers under forty. Her short stories and essays have appeared in a range of publications, and she followed up* The Tiger's Wife *with her second novel* Inland.

'I'm a very superstitious person.
When *The Tiger's Wife* was shortlisted,
I was touring with the book, and I
remember having to tell myself to
really feel this moment, even if it led
to my being struck by a falling anvil
(as good fortune always seems to). At
the prize ceremony, I felt out of body,
looking over at myself in surprise
and disbelief. Winning gave me
the emotional licence to think
of writing as my work. That
was invaluable.'

Téa Obreht

'An exceptional book…
Obreht's powers of observation
and her understanding of the
world are remarkable.'

Bettany Hughes, Chair of Judges 2011

'Be a person with knowledge,
not just opinions.'

—

Bernardine Evaristo

the song
of achilles
madeline
miller

2012

Greece in the age of heroes. Patroclus, an awkward young prince, has been exiled to the court of King Peleus and his perfect son Achilles. Despite their differences, the boys develop a tender friendship, a bond which blossoms into something deeper as they grow into young men.

But when Helen of Sparta is kidnapped, Achilles is dispatched to distant Troy to fulfil his destiny. Torn between love and fear for his friend, Patroclus follows, little knowing that the years to come will test everything they hold dear.

Madeline Miller's debut novel, The Song of Achilles, *was also shortlisted for the Stonewall Writer of the Year. It was an instant* New York Times *bestseller, and was translated into twenty-five languages. Her second novel,* Circe, *was shortlisted for the 2019 Women's Prize for Fiction and was an international bestseller. Miller holds an MA in Classics from Brown University, and she taught Latin, Greek and Shakespeare to high school students for over a decade. Her essays have appeared in publications including the* Guardian, Wall Street Journal, Lapham's Quarterly *and* NPR.org. *She lives outside Philadelphia.*

'I heard I was on the shortlist on the day
I was speaking at Ann Patchett's bookstore
in Nashville, Parnassus Books. Ann was
also shortlisted for *State of Wonder*,
and she was so generous and supportive –
right down to lending me her orange dress
to wear to the ceremony. When I won,
I felt a knee-buckling gratitude, but I
didn't even know then how significant
it was going to be. Now, nearly a decade
later, I can see the tremendous impact
on my life and work. It gave me credibility,
confidence and a passionate community
that I am honoured to be counted among.'

Madeline Miller

'This is a more than worthy
winner – original, passionate,
inventive and uplifting.'

Joanna Trollope, Chair of Judges 2012

may
we be
forgiven
a.m.
homes

2013

Harry has spent a lifetime watching his younger
brother, George – taller, smarter and more successful,
a high-flying TV executive – acquire a covetable
wife, two kids and a beautiful home. But Harry,
a historian and Nixon scholar, also knows George
has a murderous temper, and when George loses
control the result is an act so shocking that both
brothers are hurled into entirely new lives, in which
they both must seek absolution.

A.M. Homes is the author of two collections of short stories,
Things You Should Know *and* The Safety of Objects,
the novels Music for Torching, The End of Alice,
In a Country of Mothers, Jack *and the bestselling*
This Book Will Save Your Life, *and the highly acclaimed*
memoir, The Mistress's Daughter, *all published by Granta*
Books. She is a contributing editor to Vanity Fair *and writes*
frequently on arts and culture for numerous magazines
and newspapers. She lives in New York City.

'It was thrilling and unexpected –
and that was before I won. Hilary
Mantel was on the shortlist, and
had already won the Man Booker
Prize and the Costa Prize that year.
There was every reason to think
she or any of the other wonderful
writers would win. The Women's
Prize is one of the major highlights
of my career, and in some ways it
still doesn't quite feel real. It came
at a time just after my father had
died, and things were difficult with
my family, so the vote of support by
others meant an enormous amount.'

A.M. Homes

'A dazzling, original, viscerally funny
black comedy – a subversion of the
American dream.'

Miranda Richardson, Chair of Judges 2013

'We write to taste life
twice, in the moment
and in retrospect.'
—

Anaïs Nin (1903–1977)

a girl is a half-formed thing

eimear mcbride

2014

This debut novel tells the story of a young woman's relationship with her brother and the long shadow cast by his childhood brain tumour. It is not so much a stream of consciousness as an unconsciousness railing against a life that makes little sense, forming a shocking and intimate insight into the thoughts, feelings and chaotic sexuality of a young and isolated protagonist. To read *A Girl is a Half-formed Thing* is to plunge into the narrator's head, experiencing her world first-hand. This isn't always comfortable – but it is always a revelation.

Eimear McBride trained at Drama Centre London. As well as the Women's Prize, A Girl is a Half-formed Thing *received a number of awards, including the Goldsmiths Prize and Irish Novel of the Year. In 2017 McBride was awarded the inaugural Creative Fellowship of the Beckett Research Centre, University of Reading. Her other novels are* The Lesser Bohemians *and* Strange Hotel. *She occasionally writes and reviews for the* Guardian, *the* Times Literary Supplement *and the* New Statesman.

'No one thought I'd win. I certainly
didn't, so I had a grand old time the
night before at the readings, and was
feeling rather the worse for wear on
the day of the ceremony. I thought it
would be a last hurrah for the book
and that I should enjoy it, which I was
doing until the moment my name was
read out. Then I thought I was going
to keel over. Everything changed after
that. It changed the public aspect of
my working life enormously, for better
and worse. Mostly for better. But, more
importantly, it bought me time to write.'

Eimear McBride

'An amazing and ambitious first novel
that impressed the judges with its
inventiveness and energy.'

Helen Fraser, Chair of Judges 2014

how to
be both
ali
smith

2015

This is a novel all about art's versatility. Borrowing from painting's fresco technique to make an original literary double-take, it's a fast-moving, genre-bending conversation between forms, times, truths and fictions. There's a renaissance artist of the 1460s. There's the child of a child of the 1960s. Two tales of love and injustice twist into a singular yarn where time gets timeless, structural gets playful, knowing gets mysterious, fictional gets real – and all life's givens get given a second chance.

Ali Smith was born in Inverness in 1962. She is the author of five short story collections, two works of non-fiction, seven plays and ten novels, including most recently Autumn, Winter, Spring *and* Summer *in the 'Seasonal Quartet'. As well as the Women's Prize,* How to Be Both *won the Goldsmiths Prize and the Costa Novel of the Year Award.* Hotel World *and* The Accidental *were both shortlisted for the Women's Prize, and she has also been shortlisted once for the Orwell Prize and four times for the Booker Prize. Ali Smith lives in Cambridge.*

'It was as if someone had put me
in the basket of a hot-air balloon.
The Women's Prize for fiction is
the prize that gets to the places that
other prizes don't get. It always has.
It has a radar out on the world that
the other prizes sometimes just miss.'

Ali Smith

'[Ali Smith] is a literary genius…
It reminded me of what it felt like
reading Virginia Woolf, James Joyce,
all of the greats.'

Shami Chakrabarti, Chair of Judges 2015

'Literature is about nuance
and understanding the
intricacies of life.'
—

Aminatta Forna, 2017 Judge

'This is a tip given to me by
Margaret Atwood. When
you sit at the desk all morning
looking at the page and you
don't write anything –
that's writing too.'

Valerie Martin, 2003 Winner

' There are no wasted drafts. Writing can often feel quite Sisyphean – it's baffling and disheartening to have less to show after a day's work than you had before you started. But everything you throw away is just as valuable as everything you keep.'

Téa Obreht, 2011 Winner

the
glorious
heresies
lisa
mcinerney

2016

We all do stupid things when we're kids. Ryan Cusack's
grown up faster than most – being the oldest of six
with a dead mum and an alcoholic dad will do that
for you. And nobody says Ryan's stupid. Not even
behind his back.

It's the people around him who are the problem.
The gangland boss using his dad as a 'cleaner'.
The neighbour who says she's trying to help but
maybe wants something more than that.
The prostitute searching for the man she never knew
she'd miss until he disappeared without trace one night…

The only one on Ryan's side is his girlfriend Karine.
If he blows that, he's all alone. But the truth is,
you don't know your own strength till you need it.

*Lisa McInerney is a novelist, short story writer and blogger,
whose work has featured in* Winter Papers, The Stinging Fly,
Granta, *the* Guardian, Le Monde, *the* Irish Times, *BBC
Radio 4 and various anthologies. Her story 'Navigation' was
longlisted for the 2017 Sunday Times EFG Short Story Award.
As well as the Women's Prize, her debut novel* The Glorious
Heresies *won the 2016 Desmond Elliott Prize. Her second novel,*
The Blood Miracles, *won the 2018 RSL Encore Award.*

'*The Glorious Heresies* was my first book, and to be honest I wasn't sure it was any good. It's surprising how quickly the whirlwind's upon you. It's not meant to mean so much, but when it's your first novel, and you've been far, far outside the publishing world all of your life, it means an awful lot. It marks a turning point. Writing is such a solitary, uncertain occupation.

I spend more time doubting myself than feeling sure about myself. But when it gets really bad, I can look at Bessie [the trophy] and think, "Well, no one can take this away from me."'

Lisa McInerney

'A superbly original, compassionate novel that delivers insights into the very darkest of lives through humour and skilful storytelling.'

Margaret Mountford, Chair of Judges 2016

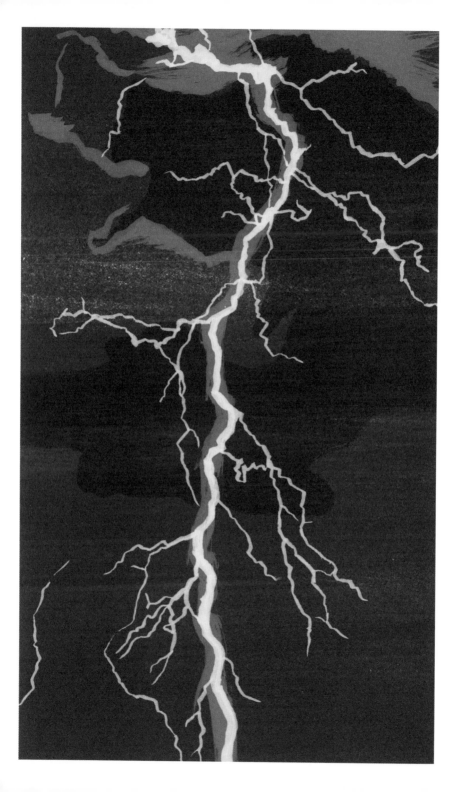

the
power
naomi
alderman

2017

Suddenly – tomorrow or the day after – girls find that with a flick of their fingers they can inflict agonising pain and even death. With this single twist, the four lives at the heart of Naomi Alderman's extraordinary, visceral novel are utterly transformed, and we look at the world in an entirely new light.

What if the power were in women's hands?

Naomi Alderman is the author of three previous novels: Disobedience, *which won the Orange Award for New Writers,* The Lessons *and* The Liars' Gospel. *She was selected for Granta's once-a-decade list of Best of Young British Novelists and Waterstones' Writers for the Future. She presents* Science Stories *on BBC Radio 4, she is Professor of Creative Writing at Bath Spa University and she is the co-creator and lead writer of the bestselling smartphone audio adventure app and book* Zombies, Run! *She lives in London.*

'Winning is a seal of approval; the prize
has gravitas and seriousness. Foreign
publishers suddenly found me much
more interesting. When trying to sell
The Power internationally my agent had
heard from one Scandinavian publisher
that "we don't need any more feminist
science fiction in our country, we have
Margaret Atwood". Suddenly they
found they might have room for two
pieces of feminist science fiction.'

Naomi Alderman

'The judges and I were thrilled to make
this decision… we kept returning to
Naomi Alderman's brilliantly imagined
dystopia – her big ideas and her
fantastic imagination.'

Tessa Ross, Chair of Judges 2017

'Lock up your libraries
if you like; but there is no
gate, no lock, no bolt that
you can set upon the
freedom of my mind.'
—

Virginia Woolf (1882–1941)

home
fire
kamila
shamsie

2018

Isma is free. After years spent raising her twin siblings in the wake of their mother's death, she resumes a dream long deferred – studying in America. But she can't stop worrying about Aneeka, her beautiful, headstrong sister back in London, or their brother, Parvaiz, who's disappeared in pursuit of his own dream – to prove himself to the dark legacy of the jihadist father he never knew.

Then Eamonn enters the sisters' lives. Handsome and privileged, he inhabits a London which is worlds away from theirs. As the son of a powerful British Muslim politician, Eamonn has his own birthright to live up to – or defy. The fates of these two families are inextricably, devastatingly entwined in this searing novel that asks: what sacrifices will we make in the name of love?

Kamila Shamsie was born in 1973 in Pakistan. She is the author of six other novels: In the City by the Sea, Kartography *(both shortlisted for the John Llewellyn Rhys Prize)*, Salt and Saffron, Broken Verses, Burnt Shadows *(shortlisted for the Women's Prize) and* A God in Every Stone *(also shortlisted for the Women's Prize). In 1999 she received the Prime Minister's Award for Literature, and in 2004 the Patras Bokhari Award, both awarded by the Pakistan Academy of Letters. Shamsie is a Fellow of the Royal Society of Literature, and lives in London.*

'I've been shortlisted twice before –
I know that's the point when you really
should just enjoy it, because winning
a prize is always a far more unlikely
than likely event. Still, I won't pretend
the winning didn't feel really wonderful.
It still feels profoundly moving.
But when you're at your desk, it really
doesn't matter what happened with the
last book. You are, as always, that writer
looking at the blank page, wondering
how to fill it.'

Kamila Shamsie

'*Home Fire* is about identity, conflicting
loyalties, love and politics. And it
sustains mastery of its themes and its
form. It is a remarkable book which
we passionately recommend.'

Sarah Sands, Chair of Judges 2018

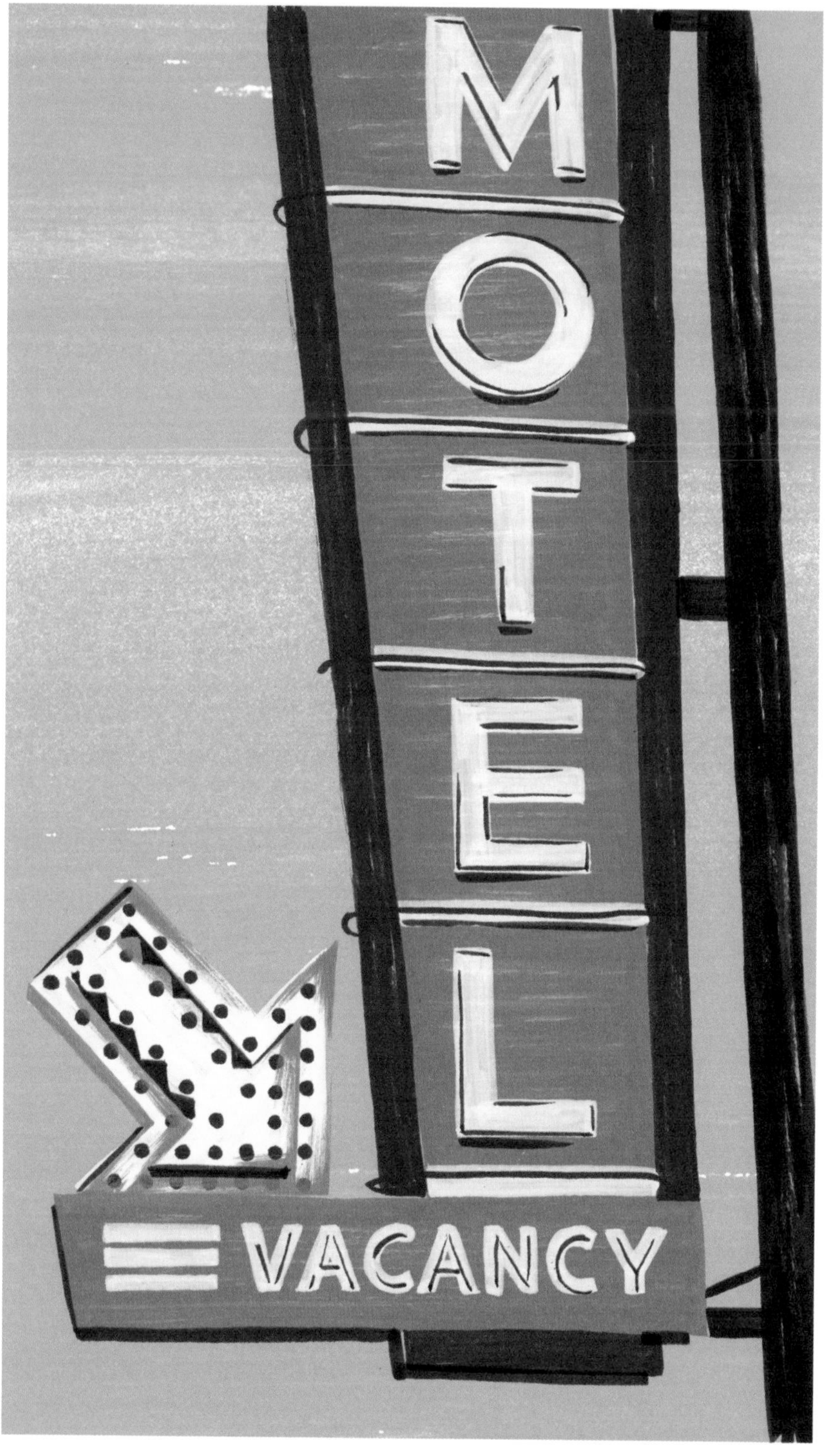
MOTEL
VACANCY

an

american

marriage

tayari

jones

2019

Newlyweds Celestial and Roy are the embodiment of the American Dream. He is a young executive, and she is an artist on the brink of an exciting career. Until one day they are ripped apart by circumstances neither could have imagined. Roy is arrested and sentenced to twelve years for a crime Celestial knows he didn't commit.

Devastated and unmoored, Celestial finds herself struggling to hold on to the love that has been her centre, taking comfort in Andre, their closest friend. When Roy's conviction is suddenly overturned, he returns home ready to resume their life together.

A masterpiece of storytelling, *An American Marriage* offers a profoundly insightful look into the hearts and minds of three unforgettable characters who are at once bound together and separated by forces beyond their control.

Tayari Jones is the internationally bestselling author of four novels, including An American Marriage, *which was an Oprah's Book Club Selection and featured on Barack Obama's summer reading list, and* Silver Sparrow. *She is currently Professor of Creative Writing at Emory University and is also the Andrew Dickson White Professor-at-Large at Cornell University. She lives in Atlanta, Georgia.*

'The Women's Prize was created because women were excluded from the world of literary accolades; in the last twenty-five years there has been tremendous progress, but female writers still face unique challenges. I am proud to have won. The shortlist was formidable and I was buoyed merely to be in the company of such artists and thinkers.'

Tayari Jones

'This is an exquisitely intimate portrait of a marriage shattered by racial injustice. It is a story of love, loss and loyalty, the resilience of the human spirit painted on a big political canvas – that shines a light on today's America.'

Kate Williams, Chair of Judges 2019

'It seems to me we can never give up longing and wishing while we are still alive. There are certain things we feel to be beautiful and good, and we must hunger for them.'

—

George Eliot/Mary Ann Evans (1819–1880)

hamnet

maggie o'farrell

On a summer's day in 1596, a young girl in Stratford-
upon-Avon takes to her bed with a fever. Her twin
brother Hamnet searches everywhere for help.
Why is nobody at home?

Their mother Agnes is over a mile away, in the garden
where she grows medicinal herbs. Their father
is working in London. Neither parent knows that
one of the children will not survive the week.

Hamnet is a novel inspired by the son of a famous
playwright. It is a story of the bond between twins,
and of a marriage pushed to the brink by grief.
It is also the story of a kestrel and its mistress; a flea
that boards a ship in Alexandria; and a glove-maker's
son who flouts convention in pursuit of the woman
he loves. Above all, it is a tender and unforgettable
reimagining of a boy whose life has been all but
forgotten, but whose name was given to one of
the most celebrated plays ever written.

Maggie O'Farrell is the author of the Sunday Times *no. 1
bestselling memoir,* I Am, I Am, I Am, *and eight novels:* After
You'd Gone, My Lover's Lover, The Distance Between
Us, *which won a Somerset Maugham Award,* The Vanishing
Act of Esme Lennox, The Hand That First Held Mine,
which won the 2010 Costa Novel Award, Instructions for
a Heatwave, *which was shortlisted for the 2013 Costa Novel
Award,* This Must Be the Place, *which was shortlisted for the
2016 Costa Novel Award, and* Hamnet. *She lives in Edinburgh.*

'It's an amazing feeling, and the judges are women whose opinions I really respect. I want to run out into the garden and howl at the moon! Looking through the rosta of twenty-five of winners I see so many writers and books that have sustained and inspired me throughout my whole writing career. I'm moved and honoured.'

Maggie O'Farrell, 2020 winner

'The euphoria of being in the same room for the final judging meeting was quickly eclipsed by the excitement we all feel about this exceptional winner. *Hamnet*, while set long ago, like all truly great novels expresses something profound about the human experience that seems both extraordinarily current and at the same time, enduring.'

Martha Lane Fox, Chair of Judges 2020

'Fill your life with diverse
and dynamic conversation.
Conversation is the workshop
of all good writing. It is in your
interest to spend time with
interesting, funny, thoughtful
people who speak candidly.
Order the second bottle
of wine in the bar, stay for
another cup of tea at their
kitchen table. Keep listening,
sharing, riffing, questioning
and talking. These anecdotes,
observations and opinions will
help you build whole worlds
from scratch. Much is said
of how important isolation
and quiet is for a writer,
but I believe that conversation
is just as informative.'

—

Dolly Alderton, 2019 Judge

'My key tip would be not
to try to please any perceived
"market", but to write what
your imagination gets excited
by – to separate the idea
of "career" or "making
a living" from the idea
of your own writing.'

Kate Grenville, 2001 Winner

APPENDIX I

Women's Prize for Fiction Shortlists and Judging Panels
1996–2020

Angie Cruz   *Dominicana*
       Bernardine Evaristo   *Girl, Woman, Other*
       Natalie Haynes   *A Thousand Ships*
       Hilary Mantel   *The Mirror and the Light*
       Maggie O'Farrell   *Hamnet* (winner)
       Jenny Offill   *Weather*

Judges: Martha Lane Fox (Chair), Scarlett Curtis, Melanie Eusebe,
Viv Groskop, Paula Hawkins

Pat Barker   *The Silence of the Girls*
       Oyinkan Braithwaite   *My Sister, the Serial Killer*
       Anna Burns   *Milkman*
       Diana Evans   *Ordinary People*
       Tayari Jones   *An American Marriage* (winner)
       Madeline Miller   *Circe*

Judges: Kate Williams (Chair), Arifa Akbar, Dolly Alderton,
Leyla Hussein, Sarah Wood

Elif Batuman   *The Idiot*
       Jessie Greengrass   *Sight*
       Imogen Hermes Gowar   *The Mermaid and Mrs Hancock*
       Meena Kandasamy   *When I Hit You*
       Kamila Shamsie   *Home Fire* (winner)
       Jesmyn Ward   *Sing, Unburied, Sing*

Judges: Sarah Sands (Chair), Anita Anand, Katie Brand,
Catherine Mayer, Imogen Stubbs

Ayobami Adebayo   *Stay With Me*
       Naomi Alderman   *The Power* (winner)
       Linda Grant   *The Dark Circle*
       C.E. Morgan   *The Sport of Kings*
       Gwendoline Riley   *First Love*
       Madeleine Thien   *Do Not Say We Have Nothing*

Judges: Tessa Ross (Chair), Sam Baker, Katie Derham,
Aminatta Forna, Sara Pascoe

2006

Nicole Krauss	*The History of Love*
Hilary Mantel	*Beyond Black*
Ali Smith	*The Accidental*
Zadie Smith	*On Beauty* (winner)
Carrie Tiffany	*Everyman's Rules for Scientific Living*
Sarah Waters	*The Night Watch*

Judges: Martha Kearney (Chair), Jenny Eclair, Claire Fox, India Knight, Jacqueline Wilson

2005

Joolz Denby	*Billie Morgan*
Jane Gardam	*Old Filth*
Sheri Holman	*The Mammoth Cheese*
Marina Lewycka	*A Short History of Tractors in Ukrainian*
Maile Meloy	*Liars and Saints*
Lionel Shriver	*We Need to Talk About Kevin* (winner)

Judges: Jenni Murray (Chair), Jo Brand, Joanne Harris, Jude Kelly, Moira Stuart

2004

Margaret Atwood	*Oryx and Crake*
Shirley Hazzard	*The Great Fire*
Andrea Levy	*Small Island* (winner)
Chimamanda Ngozi Adichie	*Purple Hibiscus*
Gillian Slovo	*Ice Road*
Rose Tremain	*The Colour*

Judges: Sandi Toksvig (Chair), Karen Cunningham, Helena Kennedy, Katharine Viner, Minette Walters

2003

Anne Donovan	*Buddha Da*
Shena Mackay	*Heligoland*
Valerie Martin	*Property* (winner)
Carol Shields	*Unless*
Zadie Smith	*The Autograph Man*
Donna Tartt	*The Little Friend*

Judges: Ahdaf Soueif (Chair), Sophie Dahl, Nicolette Jones, Annalena McAfee, Dr Margaret Reynolds

2002

Anna Burns	*No Bones*
Helen Dunmore	*The Siege*
Maggie Gee	*The White Family*
Chloe Hooper	*The Child's Book of True Crime*
Ann Patchett	*Bel Canto* (winner)
Sarah Waters	*Fingersmith*

Judges: Sue MacGregor (Chair), Gillian Beer, A.L. Kennedy, Fiona Shaw, Julie Wright

Judges: Kate Mosse (Chair), Val Hennessy, Susan Hill, Margaret Lally, Lorna Sage

APPENDIX II

Orange Award for New Writers Shortlists and Judging Panels 2005–2010

Launched to commemorate the 10th anniversary of the Women's Prize in 2005, the Orange Award for New Writers was awarded to the best first novel or collection of short stories written that year; the emphasis of the Award was on emerging talent and the evidence of future potential. It was supported by Arts Council England and was accompanied by a bursary of £10,000. The Award ran for six years until 2010.

Judges: Di Speirs (Chair), Rachel Cooke, Bernardine Evaristo

Judges: Mishal Husain (Chair), Diana Evans, Louise Jury

Judges: Shami Chakrabarti (Chair), Clare Allan, Suzi Feay

2007 Clare Allan   *Poppy Shakespeare*
      Karen Connelly   *The Lizard Cage* (winner)
      Roopa Farooki   *Bitter Sweets*

Judges: Jackie Kay (Chair), Naomi Alderman, Katie Owen

2006 Naomi Alderman   *Disobedience* (winner)
      Olga Grushin   *The Dream Life of Sukhanov*
      Yiyun Li   *A Thousand Years of Good Prayers*

Judges: Louise Doughty (Chair), Catherine Lockerbie, Stephanie Merritt

2005 Diana Evans   *26a* (winner)
      Nell Freudenberger   *Lucky Girls*
      Meg Rosoff   *How I Live Now*

Judges: Kamila Shamsie (Chair), Margaret Busby, Alex Clark

Unbound is the world's first crowdfunding publisher, established in 2011.

We believe that wonderful things can happen when you clear a path for people who share a passion. That's why we've built a platform that brings together readers and authors to crowdfund books they believe in – and give fresh ideas that don't fit the traditional mould the chance they deserve.

This book is in your hands because readers made it possible. Everyone who pledged their support is listed below. Join them by visiting unbound.com and supporting a book today.

Supporters

Sarah Abel
Sanaa Ahmed
Tony Aitman
Avril P Alexander
Janet Allen
Kathy Allen
Rhona Allin
Helen Allton
Andrea Ammer-Schoen
Laura Anders
Eric Karl Anderson
Leigh Anderson
Naomi Anderson
Shelley Anderson
Patricia Appleton
Katy Archer
Laura Arends
Catherine Arnold
Jennifer Arnold
Tish Aroyewun
Ruba Asfahani
Cheryl Ashman
Jane Atienza
Pauline Atienza
Rachel Atkin
Sophie Atkins
Liv Auckland
Louise Bailey
Sam Baker
Pamela Ball
Erika Banerji
Nicola Bannock
Lucy Barker

Andrea Barlien
Laura Barlow
Abigail Barnett
Josie Barrett
Marilyn Barrett
Alison Barrow
Susan Barsby
Shanny Basar
Gayla Bassham
Kate Baty
Robert Beamish
Rosemary Beardow
Christine Beausire
Rachel Beck
Gillian Beer
Catriona Begg
Joanne Beirne
Ellie Bell
Imi Bell
Lizzie Bell
Rotha Bell
Ingrid Bennett
Brigid Benson
Rebecca Benson
Anne-Marie Bentley
Jane M. Bett
Carole Beu
Cathy Beyers
Dr Zulifiqar Baber Bhatti
Melanie Bien
Crystal Biggin
Kasia Bijak
Sandy Bikini

Martyna Biorka
Karen Birdsall
Tamsyn Black
Ruth Blackman
Christine Blair-Murray
Nicola Bloor
Felicity Blunt
Madeleine Boddy
Jenny Boden
Natalie Boden
Penny Bond
Amanda Booth
Sara Booth
Jane Booty
Lara Borlenghi
Eleanor Borthwick
Janette Bowen
Pamela Bowen
Laura Bowler
Sarah Bowyer
Beth Boyce
Bronwyn Brady
Jamie Breen
Thank you for being one
of my Hype Chicks!
Lots of Love, Brenda X
– Friendship, Support,
Laughter, Love, Hugs
Andy Brereton
Sue Briggs
Imogen Brodie
Angela Brown
Dr Hayley Brown

Karen Brown
Lyn Brown
Rio Brown
Sarah Brown
Matt Bruce
Thanhmai Bui-Van
Erica Bullivant
Karen Bulmer
Helen Bunker
Priyanga Burford
Ginny Burges
Lucy Burman
Johanne Burns
Karen Burns
Charlene Busalli
Stacey Rossanna
    Busuttil-Harris
Emily Butterell
Helen Buxton
Gosia Buzzanca
Vicki Caddy
Alison Cahill
Sarah Calder
Catriona Campbell
Eileen Campbell
Lenolie Campbell
Nikki Cannon
Bruna Capozzoli
Lynne Carey
Anna Jane Carling
Kirste Carlson
Liz Carr
Andrea Carrick
Kate Cartledge
Heather Castel
Anne Cater
Karen Cereso
Mall Chaney
Elaine Chaplin
Laura Chapman
Sandra Chapple
Helen Charman
Natasha Chawla
Tsveti Chernogorova
Lisa Cheshire
Kirsty Childs
Christine Church
Eileen Church
Laura Church
Charlotte Churchill
Helen Clancy
Jennifer Clayton

Hettie Cloud
Mélys Codo
Clare Cole
Jenny Colgan
Alexandra Compton
Holly Congdon
Georgia Conlon
Louise Conway
Carol Cooke
Emma Cooke
Rose Cooney
Alethea Cooper
Lindy Cooper
Cecilia Cordeiro
EM Corrigan
Rachel Corry
Gráinne Costello
Wendy Coulton
Sharon Cowan
Caitlin Cowie
Hayley Cox
Sarah Crabtree
Harriet Crawford
Susannah Croft
Naomi Crosby
Grace Crowley
Jessica Crowley
Kathryn Crowley
Sheila Crowley
Sorcha Crowley
Kathrine Cuccuru
Camilla Cuminatti
Amber D'Albert
Sarah-Jane Dale
Susanne Dalton
Emma Damen
Sarah Dannatt
Lizzy Darnill
Eileen Davidson
Briony Davies
Eloise Davies
Helena Davies
Julie Davies
Caitlin Davis
Laura Davis
Dawn Dawson
Gemma Dawson
Kalbinder Dayal
Anja de Jager
Jo deBank
Aideen Dennehy
Clare Dennehy

Elizabeth Dennis
Sheila Devitt
Cora Dibdin
Hannah Doherty
Susan Doherty
Fiona Donovan
Shona Donovan-Thoma
Kirsty Doole
Joanne Dooley
Jacqueline Drake
Isabel Drummond
Kate Duncalfe
Rebecca Duncan
Kathryn Eastman
Scott Eaton
Kirsty Edkins-Gadsby
Pamela Edwardes
Michelle Edwards
Shantel Edwards
Josefine Ejebjork
Anne Marie Eldon
Elle
Lexie Elliott
Em
Michelle English
Rose Evans
Sascha Evans
Louise Farrow
Alison Ferguson
Jan Ferguson
Laura Jane Ferguson
Lucy Ferguson
Clementine Flagg
Anna M. Flynn
Rachel Ford
Catharine Forster
Carol Foster
Susan Foulkes
Rachael Fowler
Wendy France
Daniela Franzen
Victoria Freeman
Clare Friel
Camila Fuentes Diaz
Paul Fulcher
Cal Fuller
Frances Fuller
Brooke Galbreath
Anna Ganley
Michelle Garrett
Jennifer Gavin
Gwyn GB

Lynn Genevieve
Kyrstie Gennoe
Beckie-Marie George
Louise Gibbard
Moyette Gibbons
Liane Gibson
V L Gill
Mhairi Gillen
Helen Ginn
Steve Gladwin
Rose Goddard
Tasha Goddard
Caroline Gonda
Victoria Goodbody
Rhea Gordon
Dr Sophie Gosling
Bryony Gough
Gillian Gough
Jane Gould
Donna Gowland
Summer Grant
Charlie Gray
Melanie Greaves
Chloe Green
Nicola Greer
Laura Griffin
Sophia Grace Griffiths
Ciaran Grimes
Katy Guest
Corinne Guido
Sarah Hagan Jones
Sarah Haider
Aud Jorunn Hakestad
Lizzie Hall
Christine Halsall
Katherine Hamilton
Irene Hannah
Rachel Hard
Anna Harrington
Anna Harris
Jean Harris
Jennifer Harris
Anne Hart
Nina Hart
Victoria Hartley
Arianne Hartsell-Gundy
Harriet Hastings
Laurie Haugland
Carole Hawkins
Paula Hawkins
Dominique Hawksley
Jennifer Hayes

Natalie Haynes
Lauren Heaton
Kate Helsby
Lena Henry
Elizabeth Herbert
Nic Herriot
Pat Hesp
Carisse Hewer
Jenny Hewett
Emma Heyderman
Sarah Hibbits
Jo Higson
Susan Hill
Louise Anne Hodgkins
Gilly Hodgkinson
Susan Holder
Lucy Holehouse
Jessica Holland
Ceri Holman
Sarah Holmes
Marie Hood
Johanne Hoppstock
Liz Horrocks
Fern Horsfield-Schonhut
Elena Horvit
Cathy Hoste
Fiona Hughes
Emma Hulance
Elaine Hunt
Jessica Hurtgen
Pascale Hutton
Jody Ingersoll
Aileen-Elizabeth Irons
Nicola Irwin
Triona Ishola
For Izzy - You can be any
   thing you want to be. xoxo
Caroline Jackson
Pamela Jacobs
Jayne
Penelope Jenkins
Carol Jennions
Jill Johnson
Gabrielle Johnston
Megan Johnston
Dr Wendy A Jones
Jenny Jones
Justine Jones
Kendal Jones
Nikki Jones
Zoe Jones
Reshma Joseph

Laura Joyce-Hubbard
For my Bestie - Judith.
   With love from Sasha xoxx
Louise Jury
Candice Kail
Margaret Kanu
Manjit Kaur
Carol Kelly
Hilary Kemp
Jenny Kendrick
Julie Kennedy
Nik Kennedy
Mobeena Khan
Dr Afshan Khawaja
Dina Khemlani
   Hetherington
Kate Kidd-Rossiter
Dan Kieran
Adelaide Kimberly
Anna Knight
Nancy Koeppel
Sally Krause
Leander Kreltszheim
Lizzy Kremer
Giovanna Kuwertz
Marlies Lagerberg
Natalie Laharnar
Julie-Anne Lander
Hannah Langford
Holly Langley
Linda Lassman
L. Laverick
Naomi Law
Diana le Clercq
Say Leddington
DIane Lederman
Marianne Lee
Rowena Lennon
Becci Lewis
Natalie Lewis
Velda Lewis
Rebecca Lewis-Oakes
For My Brilliant Daughter
   - Libby. Love you xoxx
Chiara Liberio
Lesley Lickley
Peta Lily
Deborah Lincoln
Orla Linehan
Gillian Lingwood
Annmarie Llewellyn
Vanessa Lloyd

Fran Long
Wendy Lothian
Aleksandra Love
Jennifer Lynch
Julie Ma
Nicole Macdonald
Linda MacIntyre
Sheila MacNeill
Louise Macqueron
Eileen Madden
Carrie Maestas
Sandeep Mahal
Marija Maher Diffenthal
Rhian Mahoney
Rituparna Mallick
Claire Maloney
Mandie
Jenn Manuel
Claire Margerison
Dr Stevie Marsden
Laura Marshall
Lou Martin
Dr. Mya L. Martin-Glenn
Helen Martins
Anne-Grete Märtson
Dianne Masri
Amanda Masterson
Joyce Matters
Rachel Matthews
Michelle Mauro
Lisa Maynard
Clare McAlister-Raeburn
Joanne McCabe
Midge McCall
Yvonne McCombie
Ruth McCracken
Sandra McDonald
Val McDowall
Caroline McElwee
Emma McElwee
Sharon McHale
Jen McInnes Winning
Peter McKay
Catrìona McLean
Louise McLean
Sandra McLeod
Isabelle McNeill
Beverley McWilliam
Bairbre Meade
Mary Megarry
Susan Meikle
Jill Meldrum

Amanda Melvin
Supriya Menon
Patty Merrick
Jenny Metcalfe
Seona Michael
Catherine Midwinter
Juliet Miller
Phillipa Mills
Katy Milne
Jo Minogue
Kelly Miotti
Emma Mitchell
Jon Mitchell
Kaela Mitchell
Sophie Mitchell
Bee Mitchell Turner
John Mitchinson
Beth Moffat
Sophie Mogford-Revess
Justina Molloy
Sarah Moloney
Isabel Montgomery
Michelle Moore
Sharon Moore
Hannah Morgan
Jane Morgan
Sarah Morgan
Siobhan Moriarty
Amanda Moron-Garcia
Susan Moron-Garcia
Amanda Morón-García
Sue Morón-García
Katy Morrish
Jerry Morrison
Sam Morrow
Camilla Morton
Cristina Mottura
Anna Mowbray
Gráinne Murphy
Susan Murray
Charlie Murrell-Edwards
Anna M. Myburgh
Mandy Myles
Joanna Nader
Sian Napier
Rani Narayan
Helen Nash
Carlo Navato
Alison Neethling
Kate Neil
Anna Neill
Susan Newcombe

Sue Newsham
Catherine Nicholls
Rebecca Nicholls
Jessica Nightingale-Randazzo
Alena Nikulina
Claire Nisbet
Siri Nomme
Laura Norton
Katie O'Connor
Jenny O'Connor-Madsen
Liz O'Halloran
Melissa O'Halloran
Harry O'Hanlon
Claire O'Leary
Vivienne O'Regan
Claire O'Sullivan
Bernice O'Reilly
Liz O'Sullivan
Ann-Marie Oates
Linda Odén
Nancy Ofori
Matilda-Jane Oke
Ellen Orange
Jan Osman
Kerstin Ots
Charlie Otter
Tope Owolabi
Ololade Oyeleye
Jennifer Ozers
Karen Parker
Katharine Parker
Vanessa Parkin
Alison Parsons
Jessica Patient
Deepali Pattani
Anne Patterson
Perdy Patterson
Luise Pattinson
Toni Patton
Vanessa Paynton
Jane Pearce
Esme Pears
Toni Peers
Bianca Pellet
Sally Pemberton
Jayme Pendergraft
Patricia Perez
Kerry Perretta
Adella Peyton
Tony Phelan
Kerry Pilbeam
Heather Pitchford

Justin Pollard
Jonathan Pool
Devon Pordage
Jacqui Porritt
Josie Powell
Kerrie Power
Liz Power
Suzana Pramanik
Helen Prendergast
Ruth Prendergast
Francesca Pridding
Charli Prime
Joanna Prior
Louise Lynda Prior
Karen Pudner
Breda Purdue
Adele Pusiol
Mary Quinn
Vikki Radford
Anna Rafferty
Nimrit Rajasansi
Janet Ralston
Abi Rana
Sarina Rana
Janine Rasiah
Janet Rawlings
Joanna Rawlins
Carol Rayner
Melanie Rees
Melinda Rees
Anne Reyersbach
Hannah Reynolds
Sam Rhodes
Diana Ribeiro
Alexandra Richiteanu
Tim Rideout
Jennie Ridyard
Emma Ries
Erin Riley
Liam Riley
Vikki Ring
Renee Ripley
Chloe Rixson
Jane Roberts
Jo Roberts
Anthea Robertson
Aliceson Robinson
Anne-Marie Robinson
Carly Robinson
Stephanie C. Roe
Helen Rogerson
Isa Romby

Eve Ronson
Rachel Rose
Joanna Rossi
Charlotte Rowland RP
Andrea Ruiz Velasco
    Hernandez
Charlotte Rushton
Sally Ryan
Alaina Rydzewski
Deborah Saffer
Ashleigh Sands
Lori Saporito
Hafsah Sarfraz
Bianca Sauer
Dee Savage
Meg Schadl
Elaine Scotter
Mel Sears
Lydia Seelochan
Ann-Marie Sefton
Qaisra Shahraz MBE FRSA
Clare Shanklyn
Fiona Sharp
Samanntha Sharpe
Imogen Shaw
Karen Shawhan
Alice Shepard
Tracy Shepard
Su Sheppard
Justine Sherwood
Carolyn Shier
Hilary W. J. Silk
Polly G. C. Silk
Emily Simpson
Sally Simpson
Marion Sinclair
Maggie Singleton
Lily Sitzia
Elizabeth Skelton
Becky Skingle
Heather Skinner
Charlene Slater
Lesley Slater
Samantha Slater
Sarah Sleath
Catherine Smillie
Emma Smith
Hilary Smith
Sam Smith
Stella Soerensen
Alison Southern
Charlotte Spence

Deborah Spiers
Molly Spink
Ellie Staite
Karen Stanton
Maureen Stapleton
Starlight and the Bear
Marina Stavropoulou
Charlotte Stemp
Charmian Steven
Dawn Stevens
Lorna Stevens
Bethan Stevenson
Emma Stevenson
Jenni Stewart
Andrea Stodieck
Charlotte Stokes
Henriette Stoll
Daniella Graham Stollery
Christine Storie
Morag Strong
Lesley Styles
Anne Summerfield
Jannine Suplee
Suzanne Sutton-Curry
Penelope Swithinbank
Catherine Sykes
Claire Synge
Gila Tabrizi
Tanya
Harri Taylor
Jean Taylor
Jess Taylor
Karen Taylor
La Taylor
Sarah Taylor
Sophie Taylor
Alice Taylor-Bennett
Helen Taylor-Bennett
Claudia te Neues
Patricia Temple
Rachel Tennis
Riley Mana Terry
Isobel Thomas
Lauren Thomas
Harriet Thomas-Bush
Kalissa Thomas-Mestanas
Tracey Thompson
Alice Thomson
Patrick Thornton
Jo Tiddy
Louise Tierney
Kate Tilbury

Michelle Tilley
Anita Tobar Henríquez
Rose Todd
Amie Tolson
Amanda Tonsgaard
Artemis Toouli
Sabine Tötemeyer
Ariane Trelaun
Marianne Tsekouras
Jennifer Tubbs
Barbara Turner
Sophie Turner
Shahela Uddin
Trudi Urlwin
Helen Urquhart
Fiona Valpy
Patricia van den Akker
Deborah van Koutrik
Beth-Anna Varley
Ruth Vaughan
Jane Vernon
Kate Vickers
Barbara Waites
Fiona Walker
Caitlin Wallace
Evelyn Walsh
Kay Walsh
Steve Walsh
Catherine Walter
Rebecca Walton
Esther Wane
Emma Ward
Lucy Ward
Julie Wareing
Sam Warren
Rebecca Watkins
Helen Watson
Kathryn Watson
Wendy Watson
Michelle Watt
Catriona Webster
Lucy Webster
Julia Weiner
Hilary Welch
Lisa Wells
Hebe Westcott
Janet Westcott
June Westley
Barbara Wheatley
Susan Whiddington
Joanne White
Annie Whitehall

Bev Whitehead
Deborah Whitlock
Catherine Whitmore
Emily Whitmore
Jolette Wiersema
Carol Williams
Dotty Williams
Emily Williams
Megan Williams
Pamela Williams
Rachel Williams
Rebecca Williams
Sian Williams
Sara Williamson
Alice Wilson
Anna Wilson
Elissa Wilson
Hannah Wilson
Michelle Wilson
Paula Wilson
Claire Wood
Sarah Wood
Jane C. Woods
Laura Woods
Lara Woolford
Joanna Wootten
Emma Worthington
Victoria Catherine Wright
Natasha Wynne
Sarah Yardley
Samantha Yates
Alison Yong
Joelle Young
P.G.C. Young
Andreea Zaman
Elena Lea Zanger
Megan E. Ziegler